G2 exam - Thursday 3rd July

Time Pieces

for Flute

Music through the Ages in Three Volumes

Volume 1

Ian Denley

ABRSM

CONTENTS

Year			Score	Part
*c.*1500	Anon.	The Rakes o' Mallow	*page* 3	*page* 1
1689	Purcell	With drooping wings, from *Dido and Aeneas*	4	1
*c.*1700	O'Carolan	Dermot O'Dowd	5	2
*c.*1710	Böhm	Rigaudon	6	2
1724	Rameau	Menuet en rondeau	7	3
1725	Petzold (attrib. J. S. Bach)	Menuet in G	8	3
1759	Boyce	Heart of Oak	9	4
1795	Attwood	Andante, from Sonatina No. 3	10	4
1823	Schubert	Waltz No. 16, from D. 146	11	5
1848	Schumann	Soldiers' March, from *Album for the Young*	12	5
1868	Brahms	Cradle Song	13	6
1874	Smetana	Vltava, from *Má Vlast*	14	6
1883	Horák	Scherzino, from *Kinder-Klavierschule*	16	7
1885	Reinecke	Gavotte, from *Five Serenades for the Young*	17	7
1886	Saint-Saëns	Aquarium, from *The Carnival of the Animals*	18	8
1893	Humperdinck	Brother, come and dance with me, from *Hänsel und Gretel*	20	8
1905	Lehár	Vilia, from *The Merry Widow*	22	9
1915	Finnish folk melody	A Rose there bloomed	24	9
1935	Swinstead	Sailor's Song	25	10
1945	Lutosławski	Zalotny (Kitten-like), from *Popular Melodies*	26	10
1949	Walton	The Music Lesson, from *Music for Children*, Book 1	27	11
1955	Kabalevsky	Prelude, Op. 61 No. 1	29	11
1961	Hedges	Father Time—Chronos, from *Masquerade*	30	12

Time Pieces for Flute

Volume 1

for Margaret

*c.*1500 The Rakes o' Mallow

Anon.

Lively (♩ = *c.*120)

Published by ABRSM (Publishing) Ltd, a wholly owned subsidiary of ABRSM

1689 With drooping wings

from *Dido and Aeneas*

Henry Purcell
(1659–1695)

c.1700 Dermot O'Dowd

Turlough O'Carolan
(1670–1738)

*c.*1710 Rigaudon

Georg Böhm
(1661–1733)

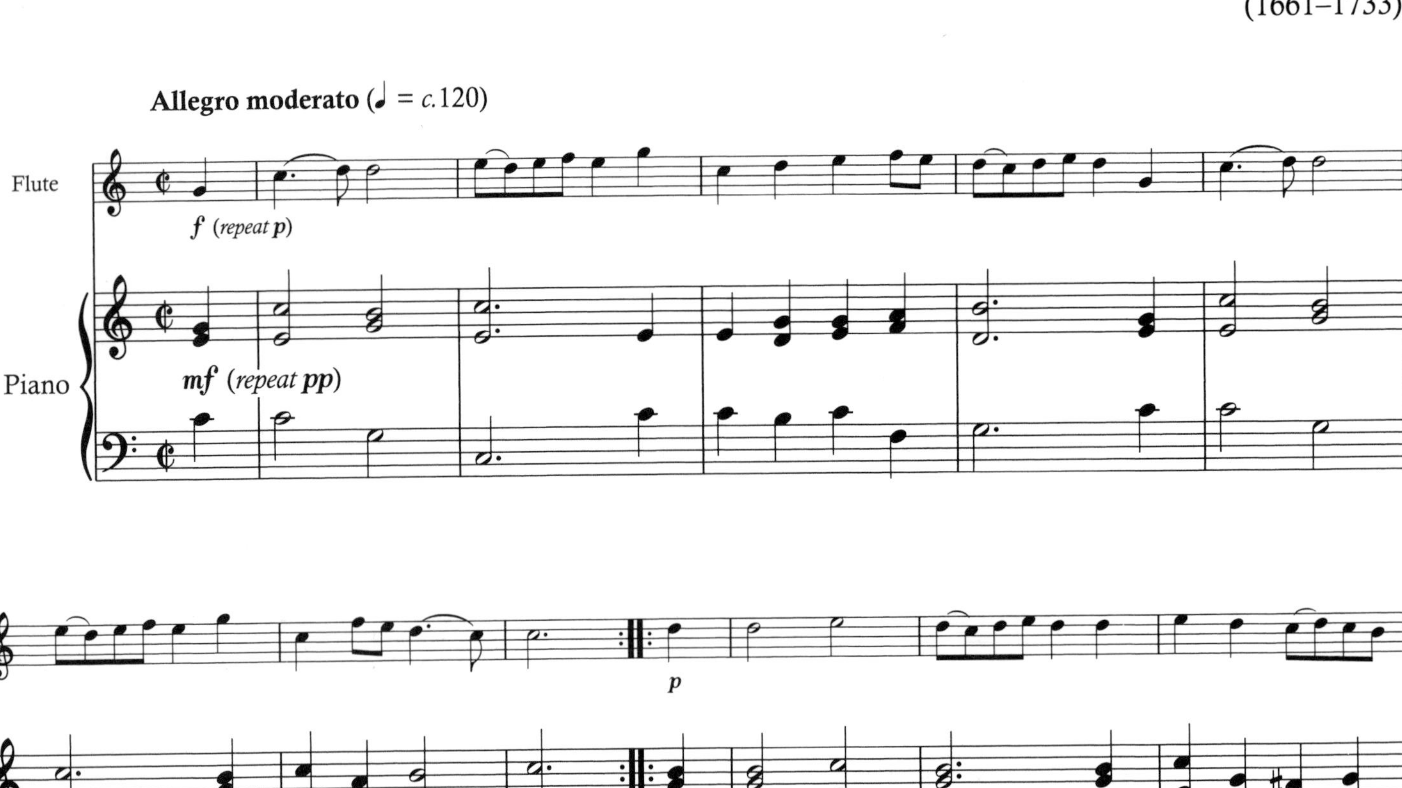

1724 Menuet en rondeau

Jean-Philippe Rameau
(1683–1764)

1725 Menuet in G

(formerly attributed to J. S. Bach)

Christian Petzold
(1677–1733)

1759 Heart of Oak

William Boyce
(1711–1779)

1795 Andante

from Sonatina No. 3

Thomas Attwood
(1763–1838)

AB 2671

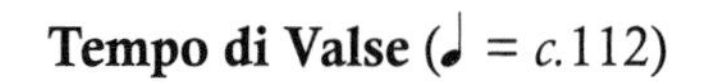

Waltz No. 16

from D. 146

Franz Schubert
(1797–1828)

Tempo di Valse (♩ = *c.*112)

1848 Soldiers' March

from *Album for the Young*

Robert Schumann
(1810–1856)

1868 Cradle Song

Johannes Brahms
(1833–1897)

1874 Vltava

from *Má Vlast*

Bedřich Smetana
(1824–1884)

sf
16
sf
sf
sf
21
mf
cresc.
26
dim.
p poco cresc.
poco rit.
mf
dim.
p
31
mp
dim.
pp

1883 Scherzino

from *Kinder-Klavierschule*

Eduard Horák
(1838–1892)

1885 Gavotte

from *Five Serenades for the Young*

Carl Reinecke
(1824–1910)

1886 Aquarium

from *The Carnival of the Animals*

Camille Saint-Saëns
(1835–1921)

mf
7
13
mp
p
pp
17
delicately
20
poco rit.
22

1893 Brother, come and dance with me

from *Hänsel und Gretel*

Engelbert Humperdinck
(1854–1921)

p
25
f
pp
p
31
pp
mp
37
p
f
44
mf

1905 Vilia

from *The Merry Widow*

Franz Lehár
(1870–1948)

mf
p
17
mf
pp
22
27
32
cresc.
cresc.
f
mf

1915 A Rose there bloomed

Finnish folk melody

Traditional Finnish melody arranged by Väinö Hannikainen, adapted by Ian Denley.

1935 Sailor's Song

Felix Swinstead
(1880–1959)

1945 Zalotny

(Kitten-like)

from *Popular Melodies*

Witold Lutosławski
(1913–1994)

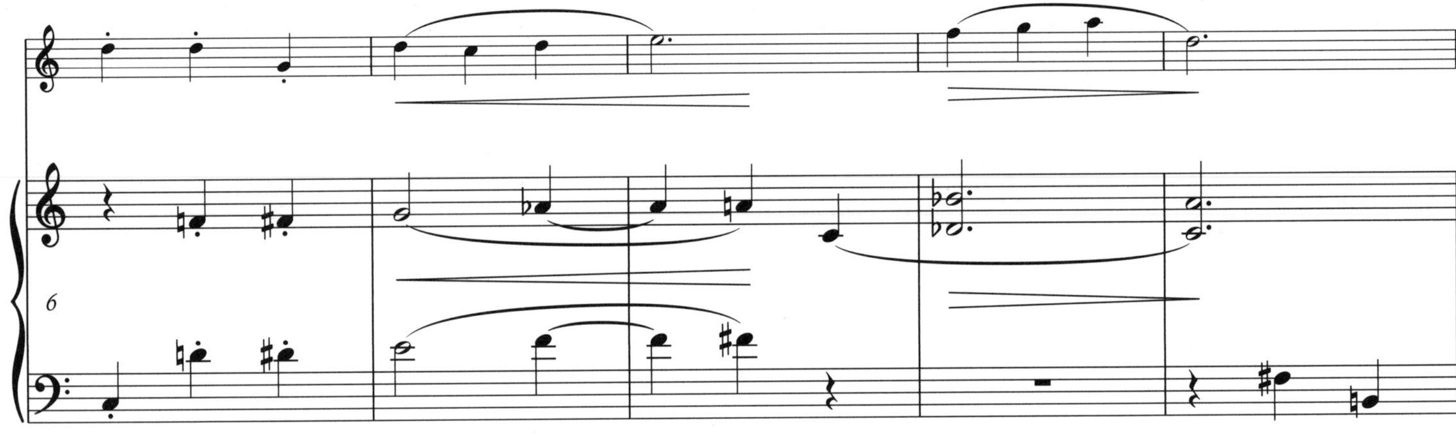

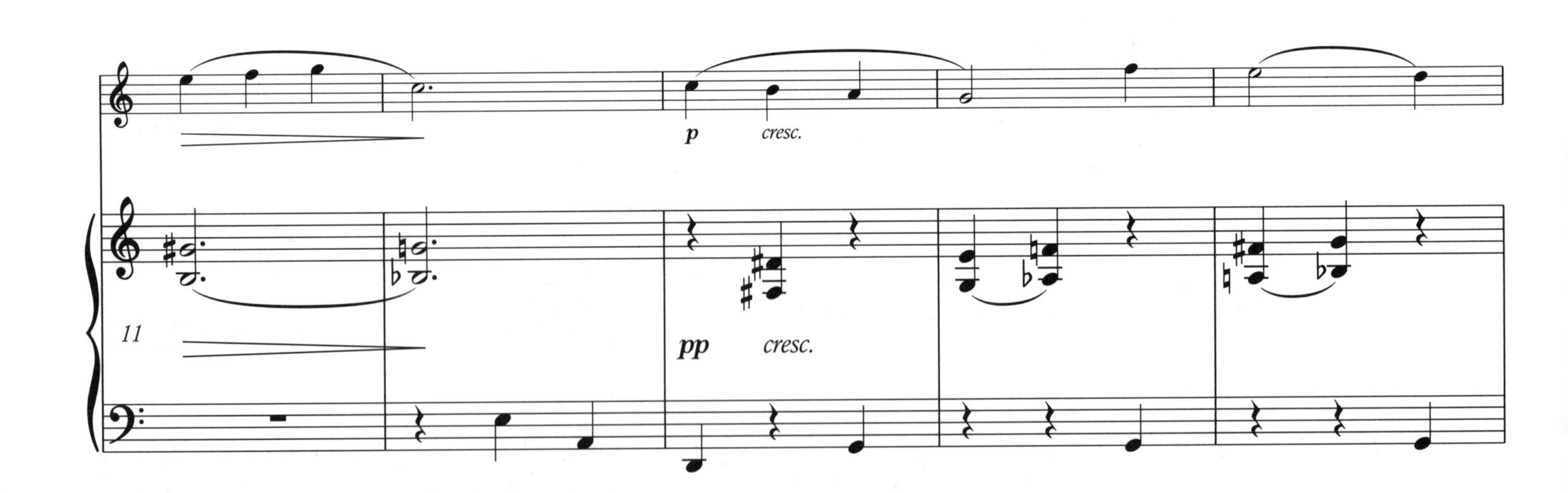

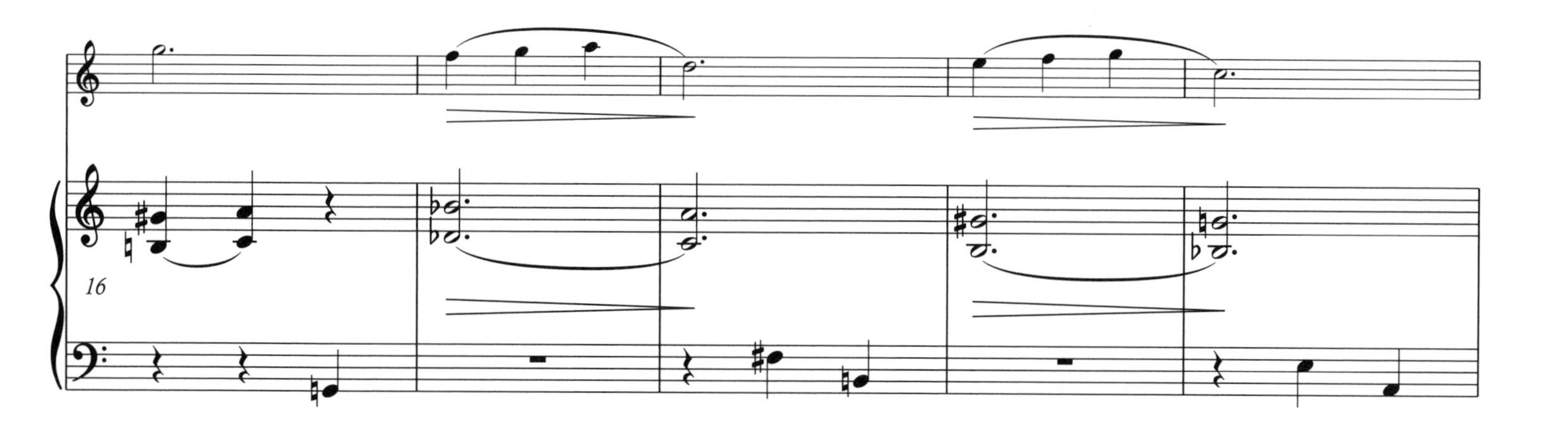

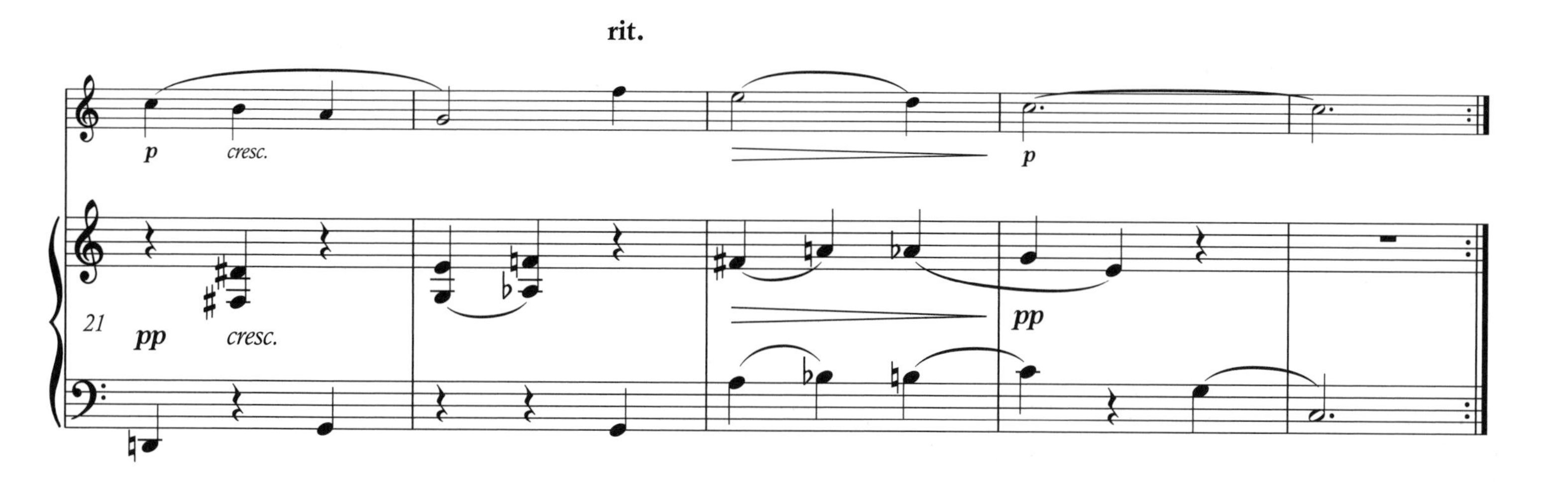

1949 The Music Lesson

from *Music for Children*, Book 1

William Walton
(1902–1983)

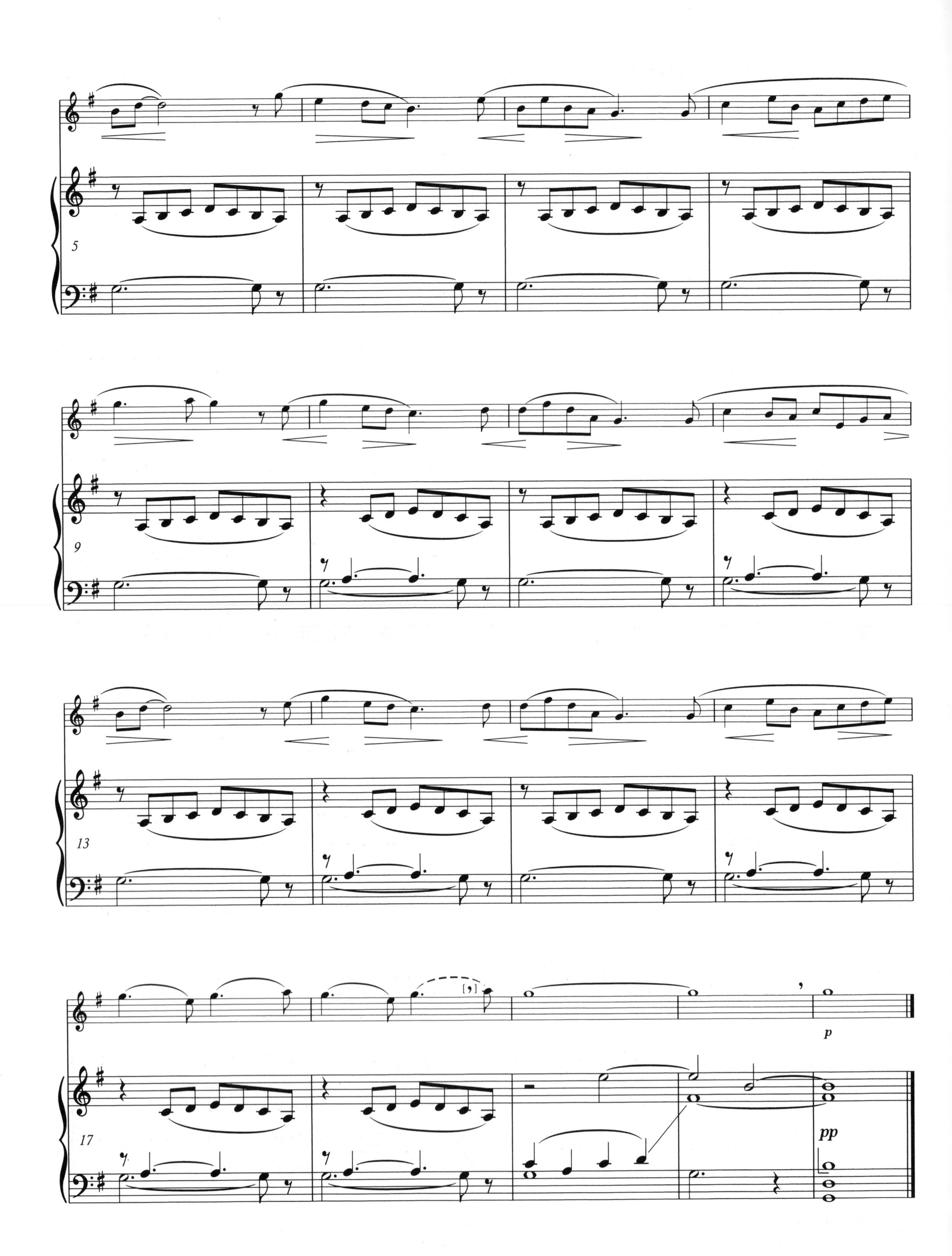
5
9
13
17
p
pp

1955 Prelude

Op. 61 No. 1

Dmitri Kabalevsky
(1904–1987)

1961 Father Time—Chronos

from *Masquerade*

Anthony Hedges
(b. 1931)

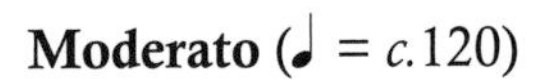

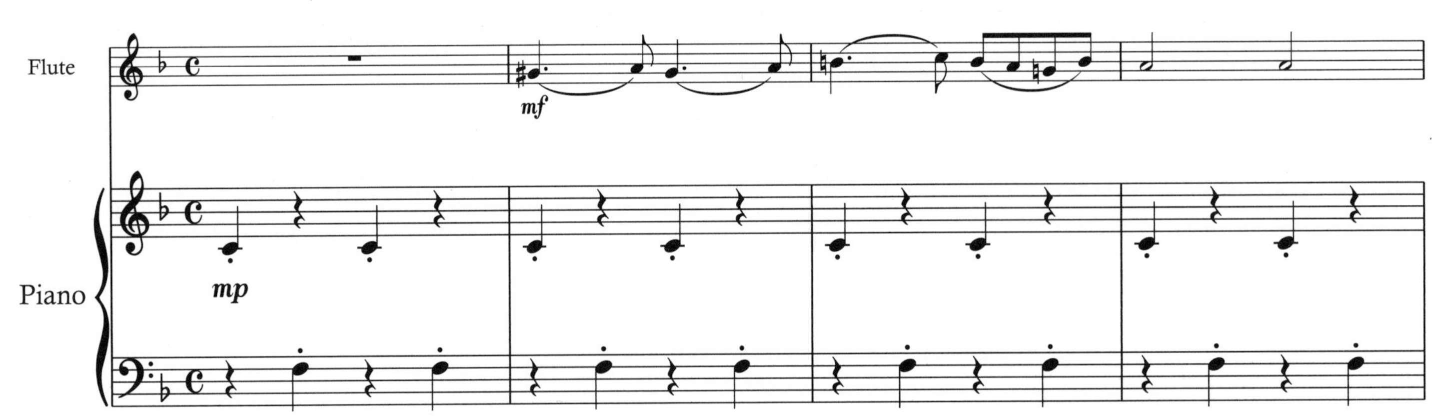

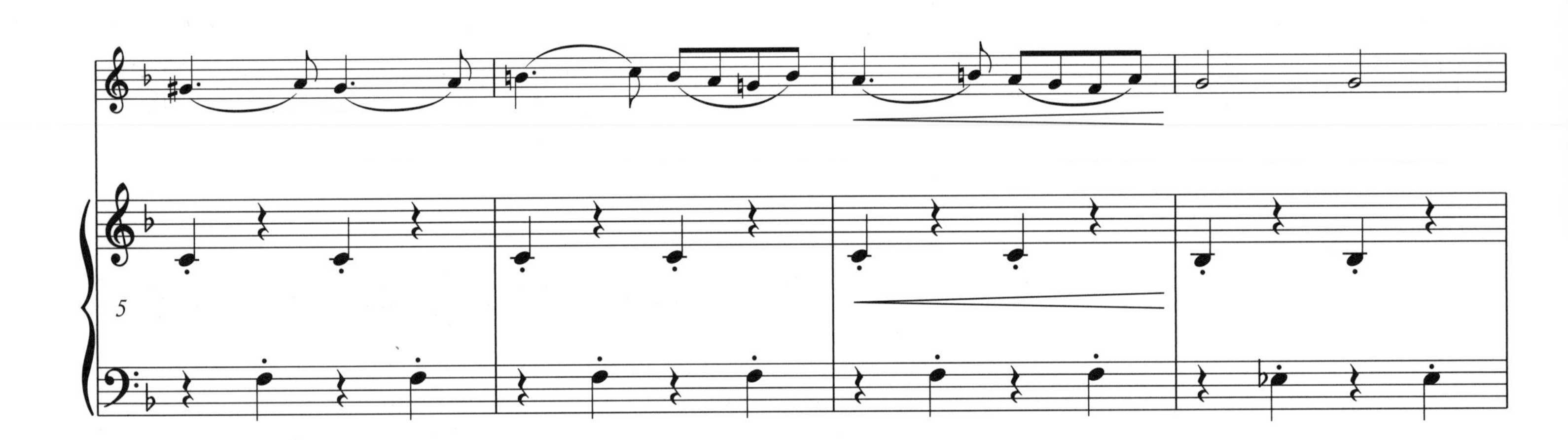

Music origination by
Barnes Music Engraving Ltd, East Sussex

Reproduced and printed by
Halstan & Co. Ltd., Amersham, Bucks., England